THIS BOTHERED THE MAN. HE ASKED THE LORD,
"DID YOU NOT PROMISE THAT IF I GAVE MY HEART TO YOU THAT
YOU'D BE WITH ME ALL THE WAY? THEN WHY IS THERE BUT ONE
SET OF FOOTPRINTS DURING MY MOST TROUBLESOME TIMES?"
THE LORD REPLIED, "MY PRECIOUS CHILD, I LOVE YOU AND
I WOULD NEVER FORSAKE YOU. DURING THOSE TIMES OF
TRIAL AND SUFFERING, WHEN YOU SEE ONLY ONE SET OF
FOOTPRINTS, IT WAS THEN I CARRIED YOU."

AUTHOR UNKNOWN